NORMANDY JUNE 44

UTAH BEACH
CARENTAN

SCRIPT: **JEAN-BLAISE DJIAN**
AND **VINCENT HAUTIN**
DRAWING: **ALAIN PAILLOU**
COLOURS: **CATHERINE MOREAU**
DOSSIER: **ISABELLE BOURNIER**
AND **MARC POTTIER**

OREP
EDITIONS

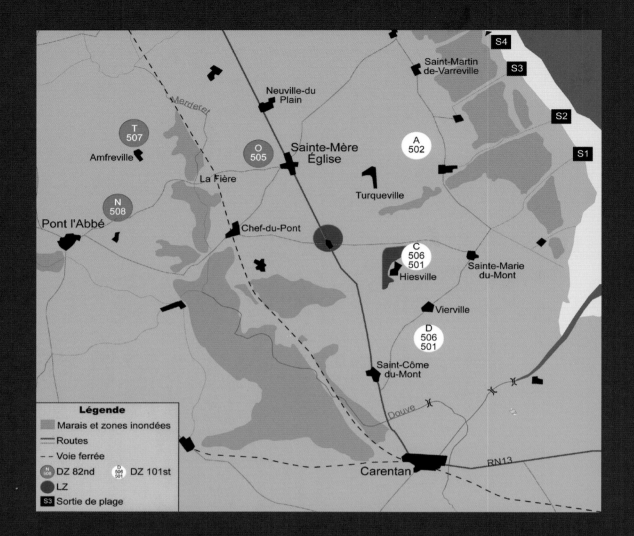

Légende
Marais et zones inondées
Routes
Voie ferrée
DZ 82nd
DZ 101st
LZ
Sortie de plage

28TH MAY 1944. ALDBOURNE TOWN HAD BECOME "ALDBOURNE BASE". THE AMERICAN PARATROOP-ERS OF THE 506TH PIR. AB DIVISION LOOKED LIKE KIDS IN A HUGE PLAYGROUND. ONLY NOTHING THAT WAS GOING TO HAPPEN WOULD BE A KID'S GAME, AND LEWIS BRANDT KNEW IT.

NOT COMIN' TO THE PUB WITH US, LEWIS?

I HAVE SOMETHING TO DO TOM... I'LL MEET UP WITH YOU LATER.

YOU OLD SO-AND-SO!

I HOPE HE WON'T LET US DOWN LIKE THAT IN PAS-DE- CALAIS...

ER, I... DIDN'T YOU SAY YOU WERE ONLY COMING BACK THIS EVENING, MR BRANDT?

I JUST REMEMBERED I'D FORGOTTEN TO DO SOMETHING, MRS BISHOP...

I HAVEN'T HAD TIME TO CLEAN YOUR ROOM YET!

DON'T WORRY, MRS BISHOP, IT'S OK...

①

MAM...

Mam

MAM, D-DAY IS CLOSE. WE ARE SOMEWHERE IN ENGLAND. I'M STAYING WITH A LOVELY FAMILY. THE FATHER IS A BUS DRIVER AND THE MOTHER IS A CLEANING LADY. THEIR SON IS AWAY IN THE BRITISH ARMY. WE FEEL SOMETHING IS GOING TO HAPPEN... YOU NEED TO KNOW THAT I'M REALLY WORRIED. WE COME FROM GERMANY SO I FEEL I KNOW THE PEOPLE AGAINST WHOM I WILL FIGHT. TODAY, I HAVE TO FACE IT, THEIR HARSHNESS IS TERRIFYING.

DIDN'T LEWIS SAY HE WOULD JOIN US ?

WELL... HIS MORALE IS PROBABLY VERY LOW !

YOU SHOULD HAVE SOMETHING TO EAT, MR BRANDT... IT'S NOT A GOOD TIME TO BE ILL

YEAH... YEAH, SURE...

MY WIFE IS RIGHT, LEWIS : TAKE CARE OF YOURSELF !

HER SON IS GOING THROUGH THE SAME... BY SAYING THAT, SHE'S PROBABLY THINKING OF HIM, WHO SOMEWHERE, MUST ALSO HAVE A STOMACH IN KNOTS...

2

28TH MAY 1944, FRANCE, MADELEINE BEACH. SECOND CLASS JÜRGEN STÜTZ IS BUILDING FORTIFICATIONS AND OTHER DEFENCES. THE LANDING WOULD TAKE PLACE IN PAS-DE-CALAIS*, MORE THAN 200 KM AWAY FROM HERE, BUT THE GERMAN HARSHNESS AND PERFECTIONISM WEREN'T EMPTY WORDS...

IT'S 6 O'CLOCK. THAT'LL DO FOR TODAY, MEN !

SEE YOU TOMORROW JÜRGEN !

KOMMANDANTUR

BYE OTTO!

HI MARCEL !

HI !

* THE GERMAN STAFF THOUGHT THE LANDING WOULD TAKE PLACE IN PAS-DE-CALAIS

③

STILL NOT HEARD FROM YOUR HUSBAND, MRS FOURAY?

NO... THEY PROBABLY HAVE NO PEN OR PAPER LEFT IN HIS STALAG!

A GOOD THING MARCEL IS HERE TO HELP ME OUT...

MAM...

ONCE AGAIN I'VE SPENT MY DAY FORTIFYING THAT BEACH I TOLD YOU ABOUT IN MY LAST LETTER. WE'RE WORKING WELL. RUMOUR IS THAT THERE WILL BE AN IMMINENT LANDING IN PAS-DE-CALAIS.

I BELIEVE IT BECAUSE THE NUMBER OF RECONNAISSANCE FLIGHTS AND ENEMY BOM-BARDMENTS HAS SIGNIFICANTLY RISEN LATELY.

WHEN I SEE WHAT WE ARE PREPARING HERE, I IMAGINE IT'S GOING TO TAKE SOME TIME TO BE CLEARED OUT IF OUR BROTHERS IN ARMS OF PAS-DE-CALAIS ARE DOING THE SAME THING OVER THERE.

BUT AFTER ALL, IT'S NORMAL BECAUSE WE ARE THE GREAT GERMANY.

4

COCK-A-DOO-DLE-DOO !

THERE YOU GO, LIEUTENANT...

FOR YOUR MOTHER, AGAIN ? I DOUBT YOUR FATHER WRITES TO HER THAT OFTEN FROM THE EAST FRONT, SON... WHATEVER, GIVE IT TO ME, I'LL TAKE CARE OF IT*...

KOMMANDANTUR

* THE OFFICER WILL READ JÜRGEN'S LETTER, CROSS OUT THE SENTENCES TOO EXPLICIT OR DEFEATIST AND WILL THEN SEND IT TO THE PERSON IT IS ADDRESSED TO IN GERMANY

ALDBOURNE, 31ST MAY 1944.

IF THEY'RE LEAVING JUST LIKE THAT, ALL TOGETHER, THAT'S IT: D-DAY IS APPROACHING...

YEAH, WELL NOT TOO EARLY! THAT WAY, THE JERRIES* WILL STOP DROPPING BOMBS...

APPARENTLY, THE DUPPOTERY AERODROME IS OVER THERE...

YES, I KNOW, WE'LL BE FLYING FROM THERE TO FRANCE...

SAUSAGE CAMP DUPPOTERY, 2ND JUNE 1944

OVERLORD

GENTLEMEN, YOUR ACTION WILL TAKE PLACE HERE, IN COTENTIN, IN NORMANDY: YOU AND THE 82ND AB DIVISION WILL BE IN CHARGE OF SECURITY IN THE KEY-POINTS OF THE REGION : FOR THE ALL AMERICAN (82D), RIVER MERDERET AND ITS BRIDGES, ESPECIALLY LA FIERE AND CHEF DU PONT, BUT ALSO THE VILLAGE OF SAINTE-MERE-EGLISE...

... IN ORDER TO PREVENT THE GERMANS FROM TAKING NATIONAL 13, THE MOST IMPORTANT ROAD OF THE SECTOR, AND VERY IMPORTANT JUNCTION.

YOU, SCREAMING EAGLES, YOU WILL HAVE TO SECURE THE BACK OF UTAH BEACH, THE CHOSEN LANDING BEACH FOR THE 4TH INFANTRY DIVISION WHICH WILL LAND AT 0630 HOURS.

*JERRIES : GERMAN

TO DO SO, YOUR REGIMENTS WILL BE IN CHARGE OF CONTROLLING THE FOUR LITTLE ROADS ALLOWING AN EXIT FROM THE BEACH BUT ALSO OF CONQUERING AND HOLDING THE VILLAGE OF SAINTE-MARIE-DU-MONT AS WELL AS CAPTURING THE TWO ARTILLERY BATTERIES LOCATED NEAR THAT VILLAGE

YOU WILL ALSO BE IN CHARGE OF THE SECURITY OF OUR LEFT FLANK, BY SETTING OUR POSITIONS AT CARENTAN

YOU, COLONEL JOHNSON, WITH YOUR 401ST PIR, YOU WILL JUMP ON THE DZ* D, NEAR ANGOVILLE-AU-PLAIN, WITH YOUR FIRST TWO BATTALIONS, AND THE THIRD OF THE 506TH

YOUR MISSION WILL BE TO TAKE OVER AND GUARD BARQUETTE'S LOCK, AND BREVANDS' GANGWAYS FACING ISIGNY

YOU, COLONEL SINK, WITH YOUR 506TH, YOU WILL JUMP ON THE DZ C NEAR HIES-VILLE AND SAINTE-MARIE-DU-MONT. YOUR MISSION: ASSURE SECURITY ON THE TWO "SOUTH" EXITS OF THE BEACH, 1 AND 2 OF SAINTE-MARIE AND POUPPEVILLE

YOU WILL TAKE SAINTE-MARIE-DU-MONT AS FAST AS POSSIBLE AND WILL HOLD THE VILLAGE UNTIL THE INFANTRY THAT WILL BE COMING FROM THE EXITS TAKES OVER. YOU SHALL ALSO TAKE HOLDY'S AND BRECOURT MANOR'S BATTERIES THAT COULD FIRE ON THE BEACH.

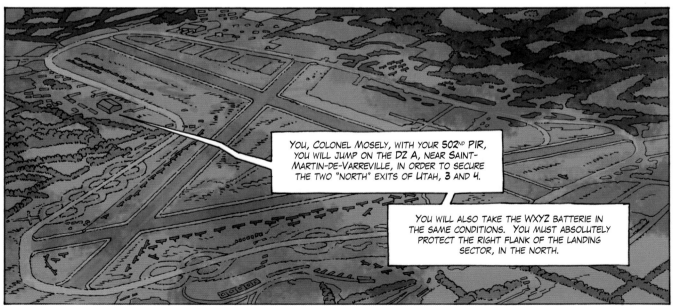

YOU, COLONEL MOSELY, WITH YOUR 502ND PIR, YOU WILL JUMP ON THE DZ A, NEAR SAINT-MARTIN-DE-VARREVILLE, IN ORDER TO SECURE THE TWO "NORTH" EXITS OF UTAH, 3 AND 4.

YOU WILL ALSO TAKE THE WXYZ BATERIE IN THE SAME CONDITIONS. YOU MUST ABSOLUTELY PROTECT THE RIGHT FLANK OF THE LANDING SECTOR, IN THE NORTH.

* DROP ZONE

3RD JUNE 1944. LIEUTENANT COLONEL STRAYER, CHIEF OF THE SECOND BATTALION, ADDRESSED HIS MEN...

GENTLEMEN, OUR JOB, THE ONE WE HAVE BEEN WAITING FOR FOR AGES WILL BE EASY: WE HAVE TO PROTECT THE BACK OF THE LANDING AREA FOR OUR INFANTRYMEN.

WE WILL BE RELEASED ON THE DZ "C", TOGETHER WITH THE FIRST BATTALION AND THE THIRD OF THE 501ST.

THE DZ WILL BE MARKED BY PATHFINDERS WHO WILL BE RELEASED BEFORE YOU IN ORDER TO CLEAN AND PREPARE YOUR ARRIVAL. EVERYTHING IS PLANNED AND WILL BE EXPLAINED TO YOU BY YOUR SQUAD CHIEFS.

WE NEED TO KILL OFF HOLDY'S AND BRECOURT MANOR'S BATTERIES BEFORE 0600 HOURS TO PREVENT THE TROOPS LANDING ON THE BEACH FROM BEING IN THE FIRING LINE.

DON'T WORRY TOM. I'LL BE YOUR GUARDIAN ANGEL, AND YOU'LL BE MINE... THE ONE SUPPOSED TO KNOCK US OUT ISN'T BORN YET!

SUNDAY, JUNE 4TH 1944. THE SABBATH...

THERE YOU GO, DUDE. AMMUNITION, COMPASS WATCH, GRASSHOPPER...

THIS TIME, THAT'S IT! JUST HAVE TO LIGHT THE TOUCH TO LIGHT THE FIREWORKS!

A GOOD THING THOUGH! ALL THIS WAITING HAD BECOME UNBEARABLE! IT WAS SENDIN' ME CRAZY!

5TH JUNE 1944. COLONEL WILLIAM B. WHITACRE OF THE 434TH TCG* BRIEFS THE PILOTS...

GENTLEMEN, YOUR "CHICAGO" MISSION WILL CONSIST IN BRINGING, THANKS TO YOUR GLIDERS, ESSENTIAL REINFORCEMENTS AND NECESSARY EQUIPMENT TO THE LANDED TROOPS OF THE 101ST AIRBORNE DIVISION.

YOU WILL LEAVE AT 0119 HOURS AND LAND ON THE LZ "E", NEAR HIESVILLE. THIS AREA WILL HAVE BEEN CLEARED OUT BY THE PARATROOPERS. BE CAREFUL THOUGH, THE GERMANS HAVE BRISTLED THE FIELDS WITH TRAPS, THE LANDING COULD BE RATHER ROUGH...

KEEP IN MIND THAT WITHOUT THE JEEPS AND GUNS YOU CARRY, THE SITUATION COULD BE SENSITIVE FOR OUR GUYS ON THE GROUND.

*TROOP CARRIER GROUP

5TH JUNE, HALF AN HOUR BEFORE THE TAKE OFF, THE PATHFINDERS EMBARKED UPON NUMBERED C-47'S. THEIR MISSION CONSISTED IN MARKING THE LANDING ZONES TO GUIDE THE PARATROOPERS...

AND ALL OF A SUDDEN, IT WAS 1100 HOURS !

AND THEN HE ASKS: "WHO PAINTED MY HORSE GREEN?"... AT FIRST, NO ONE BLINKED IN THE SALOON...

AND THEN, A COLOSSUS COMES FORWARD, TAPS HIM ON THE SHOULDER AND SAYS: "THAT WOULD BE ME, WHY?"

WHEN HE SEES THE SIZE OF THE GUY, THE LITTLE COW-BOY ANSWERS: "I JUST WANTED TO ASK YOU WHEN YOU WERE GONNA PAINT THE SECOND LAYER". HA! HA!

CAREFUL, KIDS!

6TH JUNE, 0110 HOURS, ALLIED TIME*

GOD DAMN IT! WHAT'S GOIN' ON? WHAT'S ALL THIS MESS?!!

DON'T KNOW! I DON'T KNOW, BUT ONE THING FOR SURE, WE DIDN'T LAND AT THE RIGHT PLACE! WE'RE RIGHT IN THE MIDDLE OF A SWAMP!!

PAW! PAW! PAW!

* 0210 HOURS, GERMAN TIME AND 0010 HOURS, LOCAL TIME

PAW! PAW!

HOLY SHIT! SHOTS COME FROM EVERYWHERE, AND NOT FAR FROM HERE...

CRACK!

?

BY THE HELL! IF I MOVE A MUSCLE, I'M DEAD!

UNLESS... THIS IS REALLY DANGEROUS, BUT I HAVE TO TRY TO FOLLOW ORDERS

CLAC!

CLAC CLAC!

FLASH* !

THUNDER !

WELCOME !

*RECONNAISSANCE CODE ALLOWING PARATROOPERS TO MEET UP.

11

13

TOM !

LEWIS, OLD CHAP !

WE ABSOLUTELY NEED TO FIND THE OTHERS !

SO ?

IT SHOULD BE THIS WAY... ACCORDING TO THE EXPLOSIONS, IT SHOULDN'T BE TOO FAR...

MY GOD ! IT SEEMS THAT ALL HELL IS GONNA BREAK LOOSE IN THIS GODFORSAKEN PLACE !

Sainte Mère-Eglise

TAKE CARE, TOMMY, YOU'RE MY GUARDIAN ANGEL !

AND YOU'RE MINE, DUDE !

I'LL GO HAVE A QUICK LOOK

WHAT'S GOIN' ON ?

IT'S HELL ON EARTH, LEWIS ! DEAD BODIES EVERYWHERE! THERE'S EVEN ONE OF OURS HANGING FROM THE ROOF OF GOD'S HOUSE ! AN ABSOLUTE HELL, I'M TELLIN' YOU !

STÜTZ ! STÜTZ !!

?!

STÜTZ !!
WAKE UP !

WHAT ?
WHAT'S GOIN' ON ?

THE ENEMY !
HE'S HERE !
THE ENEMY IS HERE !

THEY'VE PARATROOPED
SOME UNITS IN THE
SECTOR

WE HAVEN'T GOT ANY MORE INFORMATION FOR NOW,
BUT YOU NEED TO GO TO THE KOMMANDANTUR !
RIGHT NOW !

13

MISSED HIM, LEWIS! LET'S GET OUT OF HERE BEFORE THE KRAUTS FIND US...

YEAH! YOU'RE RIGHT... LET'S TRY AND ROUND UP THE OTHERS! WHICHEVER UNIT...

PAW!

SAINTE-MARIE-DU-MONT, 0330 HOURS

TATATATATA!!! PAW! PAW! PAW!

I'VE NEVER SEEN SUCH A CHAOS! ACTIONS MORE INDIVIDUAL THAN COORDINATED...

PAW!

HAAA!!

PAW!

⑭

ON MY OWN, I'M LOST... I ABSOLUTELY NEED TO FIND MY MATES, AND THE BEST THING TO DO WOULD BE TO GET OUT OF THIS TRAP...

PAW!

PAW!

PAW!

PAW!

WHERE DO YOU COME FROM?

I COULDN'T GET TO THE KOMMANDANTUR...

SHOTS ARE AMPLIFYING AND IT'S GETTIN' INTO A WAR FOR ONESELF, SO LET'S TRY AN' GET TO THE NEXT CROSSROAD AND HOLD IT...

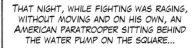

THAT NIGHT, WHILE FIGHTING WAS RAGING, WITHOUT MOVING AND ON HIS OWN, AN AMERICAN PARATROOPER SITTING BEHIND THE WATER PUMP ON THE SQUARE...

PAW!

PAW! PAW!

PAW!

... KILLED FOURTEEN GERMAN SOLDIERS COMING FROM THE SAINTE-MERE-EGLISE ROAD

15

At 0430 hours, Sainte-Marie-du-Mont was under Allied control...

But some Allies had fallen into the hands of the Germans.

What's goin' on? What is the purpose of your mission?

Don't know. I was supposed to take Vierville... I don't know the rest of the operation.

Madeleine Beach

We need to find a way to get out of here, dude! Otherwise, we're done!

Yeah, sure!

Please! Please!

What? What's up?

We want to be evacuated!

Why?

We don't wanna stay put here, sittin' on the sand... Take us somewhere else to sleep! To some place...

Take us!

They're scared to death. It must be 'cause this is the place where their troops will land...

We need to inform the captain! Quick!

16

18

BUT IT'S TOO LATE, 'CAUSE AT 0545 HOURS, THE NAVAL BOMBINGS START.

GOTVERDAMT ! THAT'S WHY THEIR PARATROOPERS WERE TRYING HARD TO STAY NEAR THE COAST ? ON THESE LITTLE ROADS LEADING TO THE BEACH...

WE ABSOLUTELY NEED TO HOLD THIS PRESSURE POINT AND TO CONTAIN THE PARATROOPERS COMING FROM THE LAND! PREVENT THEM FROM REACHING THE MADELEINE BEACH...

TATATATATA!

PAW! PAW!

PAW!

PAW! PAW!

THE GUYS OPPOSITE US ARE ACES, AND THEY KEEP COMING, LIEUTENANT! POSITION IS BECOMING DIFFICULT TO HOLD!

PREPARE TO GET MOVIN' ! WE'RE GONNA HAVE TO RETREAT TOWARD SAINT-COME-DU-MONT...

17

WHAT'S GOIN' ON LIEUTENANT ? WHERE ARE THE REINFORCEMENTS ? WHERE ARE OUR ARMOURED VEHICLES ?

WE ARE ALONE IN FRONT OF THE IMMENSITY OF A HEAVILY ARMED ENEMY ! WE'RE GONNA NEED HEAVY EQUIPMENT AND MUNITIONS !

BLAM!

AAAHH !!!

PAW!

PAW!

PAW!

THESE GUYS ARE COMPLETELY ILLOGICAL ! IT'S AMAZING !

I... I... IT'S MY FIRST BATTLE ! I...

I HAVE ALREADY FOUGHT AGAINST THESE AMERICANS IN TUNISIA AND ITALY, I KNOW 'EM ! WE ARE TALKING ABOUT HARDENED TROOPS

BELIEVE ME GUYS, WE'RE REALLY IN THE SHIT !

18

20

AT 0800 HOURS, THE LANDING TROOPS START TAKING THE FOUR EXIT ROADS. IT WAS GOING TO TAKE THEM FOUR HOURS TO MEET THE PARATROOPERS. AT 1130 HOURS, THE FOUR ROADS WOULD BE HELD BY THE 101ST.

LEWIS BRANDT AND TOM WERE STUCK AT SAINTE-MARIE-DU-MONT, HAVING TO STAY THERE WAITING FOR THE MEN OF THE 4TH.

AT NOON, THE LINK UP WAS COMPLETED ON EXIT 2. IMMEDIATELY, THE PARATROOPERS AND AMERICAN INFANTRYMEN WERE PUSHING ON INLAND.

NOW THAT WE MOVED BACK A LITTLE, WE NEED TO ORGANIZE A LINE SOUTH OF SAINTE-MARIE-DU-MONT, NEAR VIERVILLE...

19

21

THE FIRST CONTACTS WITH THE INHABITANTS ARE RATHER COLD...

I GUESS THEY'RE JUST A BIT SUSPICIOUS...

LIKE OURSELVES AFTER ALL !

Sainte-Ma du-Mont

YES, BUT WE HAVE BEEN WARNED TO KEEP OUR EYES OPEN ON THE CIVILIANS OF THE COASTAL AREAS WHO STAYED PUT... THEY MIGHT BE COLLABORATORS...

THEY'RE NOT REASSURING : THEY LOOK SO SINISTER WITH THEIR GUN IN THE HAND... I REALLY WONDER WHAT THEY'RE GONNA DO WITH US ?

DO YOU THINK THEY WILL SHOOT US ?

YOU NEVER KNOW !

ONCE THE MEN HAVE HAD A LITTLE REST, WE'LL PUSH ON TO CARENTAN

TO DO SO, WE WILL HAVE TO GO THROUGH VIERVILLE AND SAINT-COME-DU-MONT, COMMAND POST OF COLONEL VON DER HEYDTE'S PARATROOPERS...

NOT MY IDEA OF FUN, GENTLEMEN !

20

CALOVILLE HAMLET

AFTER SAINT-COME-DU-MONT, WE WILL START GOING DOWN TO CARENTAN

ONCE ON THE NATIONAL ROAD, THE TRAFFIC TO CHERBOURG WILL HAVE TO BE STOPPED

DEPARTURE AT 0500 HOURS, FIRST BATTALION AHEAD*

PAW! PAW! PAW!

PAW!

PAW!

BAOUM!

PAW!

TATATATATATATA!

WITHDRAW! QUICK! THROUGH THE CASTLE AND GABION'S FARM!

AND I WROTE TO MAM THAT WE WERE THE GREAT GERMANY!... RATHER THE GREAT DISASTER!

I'LL BE GLAD WHEN THE REINFORCEMENTS WILL ARRIVE!

BUT ON THE ALLIED SIDE, THE OUTCOME IS A DISASTER! IT TOOK FOUR HOURS TO COVER ONE KILOMETER, AND THE BATTLES AROUND THE CHURCH OF VIERVILLE COST THE LIFE OF MANY MEN...

IT SEEMS RATHER DIFFICULT TO GO THROUGH THIS WAY BUT WE NEED TO GET TO THE NATIONAL ROAD AT ALL COSTS... FORCE THE MEN TO GO FORWARD** !

*COLONEL SINK IS ADDRESSING LT-COLONEL TURNER   **COLONEL TAYLOR IS ADDRESSING SINK AND TAYLOR

21

OUR COMPANY IS BEING SENT TO THE FIRST TO REINFORCE THEM ON VIERVILLE'S ROAD TO SAINT-COME, GUYS*

YOU CAN'T IMAGINE HOW MUCH REASSURED I FEEL SINCE WE GOT THOSE TANKS** LEWIS...

FOR SURE ! I COUNTED, THERE ARE ONLY 94 OF US LEFT IN THIS DAMNED D COMPANY

BEAUMONT HAMLET

TURNER WAS KILLED ON THE TURRET OF A SHERMAN, MAJOR FOSTER WHO REPLACED HIM HAS BEEN INJURED, AND ONLY DOZENS OF PEOPLE ARE LEFT IN THE COMPANIES OF THE 1ST BATTALION...

I'M CAPTAIN PATCH...

CAPTAIN MC MILLAN OF THE "DOG"...

MY MEN ARE EXHAUSTED AND THE KRAUTS ARE MORE AND MORE SARCASTIC...

VAGUE AS WELL!... MY MISSION IS TO GET TO THE JUNCTION OF AMOUNT HAMLET...

AMOUNT JUNCTION****

PAW! PAW!

BLAM !

*CAPTAIN MC MILLAN IS ADDRESSING HIS LIEUTENANTS. **SIX LIGHT TANKS (STUART MS). ***COMPANY D, 2ND BATTALION.
****WHICH WILL LATER BECOME THE "DEAD MAN'S CORNER".

22

WHEN YOU THINK THAT EARLIER ON, OUR GOOD OLD "DOG" COMPANY DIVED INTO GERMAN DETACHMENTS...

YEP! THEY REPLIED TO ONE OF OUR ORANGE ROCKETS WITH AN ORANGE ROCKET, WE THOUGHT WE WERE IN CONTACT WITH A FRIENDLY UNIT...

THAT WAS A CLOSE SHAVE ! IT'S GONNA BE HARD TO GO THROUGH THIS WAR WITH AS MUCH LUCK !

DON'T WORRY TOM ! WE'LL ALWAYS PULL THROUGH ! I'M YOUR GUARDIAN ANGEL AND YOU'RE MINE, NO ?

CAPTAIN !
CAPTAIN !

WHAT ? WHAT'S GOIN' ON LAD ?

LOOK OVER THERE ! THERE ARE EIGHT TRUCKS LINED UP ON THE SIDE OF THE ROAD. FRIEND OR FOE ? IMPOSSIBLE TO SEE FROM HERE...

LET'S SEND A PATROL TO EITHER CAPTURE THEM OR DESTROY THEM !

GMC'S*.
THEY'RE OURS.

*TRUCKS FROM THE AMERICAN ARMY

23

BUT WHERE DO YOU COME FROM?

UTAH BEACH, SIR. WE GOT TO THIS ROAD WITH OUR GMC'S AND WENT THROUGH THE VILLAGE BEHIND US.

4-8-1 · 14

SAINT-COME-DU-MONT?... BUT THAT VILLAGE IS HELD BY THE GERMANS! THEIR SIXTH PARATROOP REGIMENT!

DIDN'T SEE ONE OF 'EM!... THEY MUST HAVE THOUGHT WE WERE WITH THEM...

WEIRD!... WHATEVER, YOU'RE IN THE VANGUARD OF THE AMERICAN ARMY IN NORMANDY!

ARE YOU KIDDING, SIR?

NOT AT ALL... ASK YOUR MEN TO TAKE COVER, WE COULD NEED YOU

IN SAINT-COME-DU-MONT, THE NIGHT WAS CALM. EXHAUSTED, BOTH SIDES HAD TRIED TO REORGANIZE THEMSELVES WHEN ALL OF A SUDDEN...

BAOUM! BAOUM!

PAW! PAW! PAW! PAW!

24

26

POSITION BECOMES DIFFICULT TO HOLD. WE'RE GONNA TRY TO PULL OUT OF SAINT-COME...

PAW! PAW!

PAW! BLOOM! PAW!

WHERE ARE WE GOIN', CAPTAIN?

BLOSVILLE AND SAINTE-MÉRE-EGLISE ARE IN THE HANDS OF THE ENEMY*. LET'S TRY TO REACH NATIONAL 13 AND GET TO CARENTAN

PAW! PAW!

PAW! PAW!

THIS CAN'T BE POSSIBLE! WE'RE FLEEING LIKE RATS FROM PLACE TO PLACE!

AT 1600 HOURS, THE LAST GERMAN DEFENDERS EVACUATE SAINT-COME-DU-MONT BY FOLLOWING THE PARIS-CHERBOURG RAILWAY...

AT 1700 HOURS, LT-COLONEL EWELL** ENTERS SAINT-COME-DU-MONT AS A VICTOR

*AT THAT MOMENT, THESE VILLAGES WERE IN THE HANDS OF THE PARATROOPERS OF THE 82ND AB DIVISION. **CHIEF OF THE 3RD BATALLION SU 506TH PIR.

25

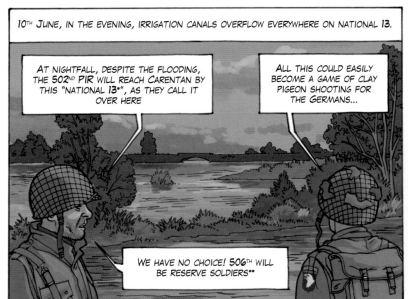

10TH JUNE, IN THE EVENING, IRRIGATION CANALS OVERFLOW EVERYWHERE ON NATIONAL 13.

AT NIGHTFALL, DESPITE THE FLOODING, THE 502ND PIR WILL REACH CARENTAN BY THIS "NATIONAL 13*", AS THEY CALL IT OVER HERE

ALL THIS COULD EASILY BECOME A GAME OF CLAY PIGEON SHOOTING FOR THE GERMANS...

WE HAVE NO CHOICE! 506TH WILL BE RESERVE SOLDIERS**

TATATATATATA!

GOD DAMN IT, LEWIS! WE'LL NEVER PULL THROUGH! WE'RE DONE! THIS AREA IS GONNA BE OUR CEMETERY... BLOODY HELL! WHEN YOU THINK OF...

DON'T THINK ABOUT IT! WE'RE ALREADY LUCKY WE WERE PUT AS A RESERVE!

PAW!

PAW!

TO PREVENT US FROM ADVANCING, THE KRAUTS ARE SNIPING AT US FROM POMMENAUQUE HAMLET, OVER THERE, COLONEL... WE HAVE TO TRY SOMETHING!

26

*NATIONAL 13 NICKNAMED "PURPLE HEART LANE" BY THE PARATROOPERS.
** TO BE PLACED AS A COVER ON A RETREATED AREA, AND WAIT TO BE SENT AS REINFORCEMENT FOR THE UNITS ALREADY FIGHTING.

WE HAVE NO CHOICE, GUYS, WE HAVE TO FINISH IT OFF! FIX BAYONETS!

TATATATATATA!

PAW!

PAW!

PAW! TATATATATATA! PAW!

PAW! PAW!

THE FIRST BATTALION OF THE 501ST HAS HAD TERRIBLE LOSSES. IT LITERALLY GOT WIPED OUT AND THE 502ND IS TOO EXHAUSTED, COLONEL...

YES, THE MACHINE GUNS AND THE CANNONS OF 88 ENEMIES WILL HAVE CAUSED MORE LOSSES THAN ALL THE REST. 506TH WILL REPLACE THEM.

LET'S TAKE OVER THIS FARM* ! IT WILL BE OUR COMMAND POST!

*INGOUF FARM

WE'RE DONE, MANFRED !!

SHUT UP !

WE HAVE TO HOLD NO MATTER WHAT ! PLACE YOURSELVES IN THE UPPER FLOORS OR IN THE CELLARS ! AND EVERY SHOT HAS TO COUNT !

PAW !

THINGS ARE GETTIN' REALLY COMPLICATED, GENERAL* ! ESPECIALLY SINCE GÖTZ VON BERLICHINGEN'S 17TH WAFFEN SS DIVISION ENTERED THE TOWN TO BACK UP THE ENEMY...

I KNOW ALL THAT, COLONEL**. AND THAT'S WHY A NEW PLAN OF ATTACK HAS BEEN ESTABLISHED.

*GENERAL TAYLOR. **COLONEL HARPER.

WE'RE GONNA ENGAGE FIVE REGIMENTS IN THIS BATTLE : 506TH WILL ATTACK THROUGH PERIERS, BY THE WEST, 327TH AND 401ST GLIDERS BY THE NORTH, 502ND THROUGH ST-COME, 501ST BY THE EAST

THE OBJECTIVE IS TO TAKE A GRIP ON ALL SIDES OF THE CITY.

THE UNITS GOING TO THE WEST WILL ALSO HAVE TO SEIZE HILL 30 AT THE SOUTH WEST OF THE TOWN IN ORDER TO OVERLOOK THE GERMANS' RETREAT PATHS.

THIS TIME, I THINK THE TOWN HAS FALLEN ! IT'S REALLY SHIT IN THIS GODFORSAKEN PLACE !

?!

YEAH !... LET'S STAY VIGILANT THOUGH !... YOU DON'T HAVE ANOTHER CHEWING-GUM, DO YOU TOM ?

PAW!

GET DOWN, I.. AAAAAH !!!

PAW!

30

WHAT A MESS, THE WAR !

IN THE EVENING OF 12TH JUNE, CARENTAN IS UNDER AMERICAN CONTROL. THE LINK-UP BETWEEN OMAHA AND UTAH IS GOING TO BE DONE...

... BUT IT IS NORMAL BECAUSE AFTER ALL WE ARE THE GREAT GERMANY. DON'T WORRY, YOU'LL SEE, WE'LL ALL BE CELEBRATING XMAS TOGETHER WITH DAD. LOTS OF LOVE. YOUR LOVING SON.

IN THE UNITED STATES, EVERY FAMILY WHO HAD A MEMBER PARTICIPATING IN THE WAR HAD A LITTLE WHITE FLAG ON THEIR LETTERBOX, DECORATED WITH AS MANY BLUE STARS AS THERE WERE SOLDIERS.

... THEIR HARSHNESS IS TERRIFYING. YOU SEE, EVEN IF THE LATTER IS FAIR, THE WAR IS REALLY A TERRIBLE THING. WE SHOOT UNIFORMS BUT THERE ARE PEOPLE INSIDE. I HOPE TO SEE YOU AGAIN, YOU AND DAD. LOTS OF LOVE. YOUR LOVING SON.

THE END

NORMANDY JUNE44

UTAH BEACH
SAINTE-MERE-EGLISE

SCRIPT: JEAN-BLAISE DJIAN
AND ISABELLE BOURNIER
ILLUSTRATED BY: ALAIN PAILLOU
COLORS: CATHERINE MOREAU

LONDON, SUMMER 1943.

GENTLEMEN, WE ARE GATHERED HERE TODAY BECAUSE THE RESISTANCE NETWORK "BRUTUS", LOCATED IN THE COTENTIN PENINSULA HAS SENT US INFORMATION ABOUT THE SITUATION THERE...

AS WE SUSPECTED, THE GERMAN CHIEF OF STAFF ARE ON HIGH ALERT. THEY HAVE ORDERED THE EVACUATION OF WOMEN, CHILDREN AND ELDERLY PEOPLE FROM THE OUTSKIRTS OF CHERBOURG.

WE HAVE LOST EVERYTHING! WHAT ARE WE GOING TO DO, GERMAIN? A WHOLE LIFE WASTED!

WAIT MOM, IT'S NOT OVER. THE GERMANS ARE STARTING TO HAVE THEIR DOUBTS TOO...

THEY'RE HAVING A HARDER AND HARDER JOB ON THE EASTERN FRONT AND THE ALLIES HAVE LANDED IN NORTH AFRICA.

AND BY THE WAY, ROMMEL AND HIS ITALIAN ALLY WERE DEFEATED BY THE BRITISH TROOPS AT EL ALAMEIN LAST NOVEMBER...

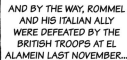 IF ONLY IT WAS TRUE, JULIETTE!

MOM, JUST LOOK AT THEM. THE ONLY THING THESE GERMANS HAVE IN COMMON WITH THE ONES WHO CONQUERED US, IS THEIR LOVAT GREEN UNIFORM.

01

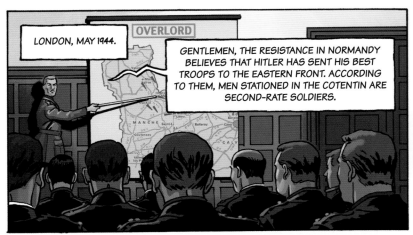
LONDON, MAY 1944.

OVERLORD

GENTLEMEN, THE RESISTANCE IN NORMANDY BELIEVES THAT HITLER HAS SENT HIS BEST TROOPS TO THE EASTERN FRONT. ACCORDING TO THEM, MEN STATIONED IN THE COTENTIN ARE SECOND-RATE SOLDIERS.

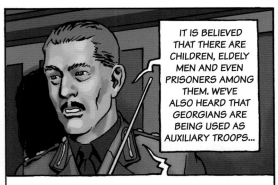
IT IS BELIEVED THAT THERE ARE CHILDREN, ELDELY MEN AND EVEN PRISONERS AMONG THEM. WE'VE ALSO HEARD THAT GEORGIANS ARE BEING USED AS AUXILIARY TROOPS...

THEY FORM THE 795TH BATTALION OF THE 709TH INFANTRY DIVISION AND ARE IN CHARGE OF DEFENDING A BEACH NEAR SAINTE-MARIE- DU-MONT.

ON THE OTHER HAND, THE NETWORK OF BUNKERS ON THE COAST HAS CONSIDERABLY BEEN REINFORCED. THEY EVEN REQUISITIONED CIVILIANS TO HASTEN ITS CONSTRUCTION.

JUST ABOUT EVERYWHERE THROUGHOUT THE FIELDS, THE ENEMY HAS DUG TRENCHES ALONG WITH ANTI-TANK DITCHES AND SET UP GUN EMPLACEMENTS, BUT ABOVE ALL...

HE IS HAVING POSTS POSITIONED IN ALL THE FIELDS THAT THE LOCALS CALL "ROMMEL'S ASPARAGUS"

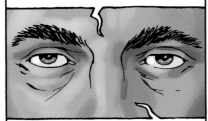
I REASSURE YOU, THE RESISTANCE CERTIFIES THAT THE FRENCH PEOPLE IN CHARGE OF THIS TASK SHOW THE MOST ABSOLUTE LACK OF ZEAL.

THE GERMANS PANIC. LAST MARCH, FEARING THAT THE LOCAL VILLAGERS MIGHT HEAR ABOUT THE GENERAL SITUATION, THEY HAD THEM TURN IN ALL THEIR WIRELESS SETS* TO THE TOWN HALL.

NIGHT OF JUNE 5TH 1944...

LOOK MOM! THE ALLIES ARE BOMBING THE COASTAL BATTERIES OF SAINT-MARTIN-DE-VARREVILLE.

YEAH RIGHT! THEY BOMB EVERY NIGHT AT THE MOMENT, I'M GOING TO BED...

* IT WAS ON ONE OF THESE SMALL CRYSTAL SETS THAT ON THE MORNING OF JUNE 5TH, THE BBC ANNOUNCED THE FALL OF ROME.

MOM! DAD!

HAS YOUR UM ... AIRCRAFT BEEN SHOT DOWN?

NO! THIS TIME, IT'S THE BIG INVASION. THOUSANDS AND THOUSANDS OF AMERICAN PARATROOPERS ARE ABOUT TO LAND IN THE AREA...

THE 82ND AND 101ST US AIRBORNE DIVISIONS* WILL BE DROPPED NEAR SAINTE-MÈRE-EGLISE, SAINT-CÔME-DU-MONT AND PICAUVILLE.

WHAT IS THE SITUATION IN THIS VILLAGE?

THERE ARE NO GERMANS HERE. THE CLOSEST ARE STATIONED IN SAINTE-MÈRE-EGLISE, ABOUT 2 KILOMETERS FROM HERE.

*13,000 MEN JUMPING OFF 832 AIRCRAFTS IN ORDER TO TAKE HOLD OF KEY ROADS AND BRIDGES, BLOW UP THE RAILWAY LINE TO CARENTAN AND ANNIHILATE SOME GERMAN COASTAL BATTERIES.

DO YOU KNOW WHERE I COULD READ MY MAP WITHOUT RISKING BEING SEEN WITH MY LIGHT ON?

COME INSIDE, WE'LL PUT A MATTRESS IN FRONT OF THE WINDOW.

THANKS BUT I WOULDN'T WANT TO COMPROMISE YOU IF THE GERMANS WERE TO SHOW UP WITHOUT WARNING ...

PLEASE! WE'LL JUST HAVE 2 PEOPLE ON GUARD, THEY'LL WARN US IN CASE OF DANGER.

SO, WE ARE HERE.

BUT I...I DIDN'T THINK I WAS THAT FAR AWAY FROM THE RAILWAY LINE AND THAT SMALL RIVER... THE MER ... MERDERET.

THE BAD WEATHER MUST HAVE BLOWN YOU OFF COURSE OF YOUR DESIGNATED DROP ZONE...

IT'S ELEVEN TWENTY.

I ABSOLUTELY HAVE TO MEET UP WITH MY COMPANY. COULD YOU TELL ME THE BEST WAY TO GET THERE?

OK. THIS IS THE SHORTEST WAY AND THE LEAST CHANCE OF MEETING GERMANS SOLDIERS....

THANK YOU.

HERE, SOME CHOCOLATE FOR THE CHILDREN.

THE DAYS TO COME WILL BE TERRIBLE. GOOD LUCK, MISS.

GOODBYE MISS, AND GOODNIGHT TO YOU ALL.

40

IT REALLY SOUNDS SERIOUS...

YOU BET IT'S SERIOUS! YOU SAW ALL THOSE PARATROOPERS IN THE SKY EARLIER ...

YES BUT BELIEVE ME, THAT WAS NOT ENOUGH TO LIBERATE THE COUNTRY!

HE TOLD ME HE WAS A "PATHFINDER"... YOU HEARD HIM, THE ALLIES ARE GOING TO LAND BY THE THOUSANDS ...

GOOD FOR US! IF ONLY THEY COULD FREE THE WORLD OF HITLER...

YEAH, BUT IN THE MEANTIME, WE'D BETTER GO TO BED AND PRETEND TO BE SLEEPING, BECAUSE IF THE GERMANS SHOW UP LOOKING FOR THE PARATROOPER, THEN WE WILL HAVE A REAL REASON TO WORRY!

THEY PUT YOU UP AGAINST THE WALL FOR LESS THAN THIS!

ANYWAY, YOU CAN ALL DO YOUR OWN THING BUT I...

BOOOM

IT...IT ... IS COMING FROM THE SEA, THE WHOLE SKY IS ABLAZE...

THESE ARE NAVY SHELLS AND THAT'S HEAVY STUFF!

YEAH BUT THERE'S MORE! LISTEN! ... LISTEN!

THEY'RE FLYING JUST ABOVE US!

0
5

WATCH OUT! THEY'RE ABOUT TO DROP BOMBS!!!

I KNEW IT! THIS... THIS IS MAGNIFICENT!

YEAH ... REAL FIREWORKS!

BANG! BANG! TATATA!

HEY! LOOK!

EXPLOSIONS AND DETONATIONS SCARED THEM AWAY!!
WE HAVE TO CATCH THEM!

NO! LET THEM GO!
THE BATTLE ON THE GROUND IS ABOUT TO START, WE SHOULD ALL GO HOME AND HIDE!

THOSE WHO WANT TO TAKE REFUGE IN PRAYER, FOLLOW ME! THE CHURCH'S WALLS WILL PROTECT US FROM THE RANDOM SHOTS!

IT'S AFTER 2 AM!

OH GOD!
LET'S HOPE EVERYTHING TURNS OUT RIGHT.

43

WHOA

WHAT? WHAT'S THE MATTER, JULIETTE?

THEY'RE ... THEY'RE STANDING OUTSIDE OUR DOOR.

THEY? WHO'S "THEY"?

KNOCK! KNOCK! KNOCK!

HEY! WE, AMERICANS...ARE THERE GERMANS IN HERE?

DID YOU HEAR HOW CONFIDENT HE SOUNDED? YOU WOULD ALMOST BELIEVE THEY'VE ALREADY WON THE WAR...

WELCOME TO NORMANDY!

I REALIZE IT WASN'T EASY FOR YOU EITHER OVER THERE, BUT...GOD...WE HAVE BEEN WAITING FOR YOU FOR A LONG TIME!

HANG ON! I HAVE A LITTLE CALVADOS BRANDY... YOU'LL LOVE IT! I ONLY TAKE IT OUT FOR SPECIAL OCCASIONS!

HEY, JULIETTE! YOU SPEAK ENGLISH, RIGHT? COULD THEY USE YOU AS AN INTERPRETER?

YES...YES, OF COURSE! I'D BE HAPPY TO!

THAT PLACE IS BLACK LANDS FARM, NEAR THE VILLAGE OF LA FIÈRE AND CLOSE TO THE PARIS-CHERBOURG RAILWAY LINE, BETWEEN FRESVILLE AND CHEF-DU-PONT TRAIN STATIONS.

COULD YOU TELL ME THE BEST WAY TO GET THERE? AND ALSO TELL ME IF THERE ARE GERMANS STATIONED IN THAT SECTOR...

HMM ! HMM ! MISS ?

I HEARD YOU SPEAK ENGLISH... MY RALLYING POINT IS LOCATED CLOSE TO A PLACE CALLED "THE THREE ELMS" ...

IT'S THERE... A SMALL PATH AT THE BOTTOM OF THE SLOPE, RIGHT AT THE ENTRANCE OF SAINTE-MÈRE-EGLISE...

OK, BUT I'D RATHER AVOID THE MAIN ROAD...

45

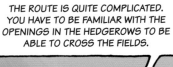

THE ROUTE IS QUITE COMPLICATED. YOU HAVE TO BE FAMILIAR WITH THE OPENINGS IN THE HEDGEROWS TO BE ABLE TO CROSS THE FIELDS.

LISTEN...I...I AM GOING TO GO WITH YOU....

NO, YOU'RE NOT TAKING SUCH A RISK ...

IN THAT CASE, EXPECT TO SUFFER MR. OFFICER!

HMM...OK....I'M SORRY ABOUT THIS BUT YOU'RE RIGHT, I DON'T HAVE ANY CHOICE...

WE'RE NOW VERY CLOSE TO SAINTE-MÈRE-EGLISE...TWO MORE PASTURES TO CROSS.

GREAT!

WITHOUT YOUR HELP, WE ...

TA TA TA TA TA TA!

THAT WAS A SKIRMISH! IT SEEMS OVER! LET'S MOVE ON.

THANK YOU MISS...AND BE CAREFUL GOING HOME.

I'LL GO BY THE "CROIX DE NEUVILLE", TO GET THERE FASTER...

IF I'M ALONE, THE GERMANS WON'T BOTHER ME.

STEP BACK KIDS! AND FAST! JUST DON'T STAY HERE!

JUNE 6, 1964

AT THAT TIME, IN THE VILLAGE, WE DIDN'T KNOW WHAT HAD HAPPENED TO JULIETTE, THE CHERBOURG WOMAN AND EVERYBODY WAS HAPPY...BUT IT DIDN'T TAKE LONG FOR THE "LOVAT GREEN" TO PUT THEMSELVES TOGETHER.

20e ANNIVERSAIRE * DÉBARQUEMENT NORMANDIE

A GERMAN COLUMN CAME DOWN TOWARDS NEUVILLE FROM EMONDEVILLE ... SOON THEY WERE EVERY-WHERE, EMERGING FROM EVERY DIRECTION...

THEY QUICKLY GOT THE UPPER HAND, TOOK SOME PRISONERS AND BROUGHT THEM TO THE CASTLE ...

THE LOCAL VILLAGERS WERE AWARE THAT EVERYTHING COULD CHANGE DRAMATICALLY. THE SITUATION HAD BECOME CONFUSING. THEY WERE LOSING CONFIDENCE....A TERRIBLE FEAR WAS OVERWHELMING THEM ...

IN THE EARLY MORNING HOURS OF THE 7TH, MOST OF THE HOUSES WERE DESERTED, PEOPLE FEARED THE GERMANS WOULD RETALIATE ...

THEY WENT THROUGH THE DE DANCOURT FARM AND THE RECTORY. THERE WERE SHOTS EVERYWHERE. THE GERMANS WERE IN A TRENCH AND THE AMERICANS WERE BEHIND A HEDGEROW ON THE OTHER SIDE.

I WAS PART OF THE RESISTANCE, I GUIDED AMERICAN TROOPS. I ...

I WAS THE ONE, WHO EARLIER, HAD ASKED JULIETTE TO TRANSLATE.

THE END.

BUT YOU...YOU WERE WITH THE OTHER VILLAGERS?

ME?

* 20TH ANNIVERSARY OF THE NORMANDY LANDING.

48

NORMANDY JUNE 44

A DOSSIER FROM **ISABELLE BOURNIER** AND **MARC POTTIER**

The day before we jumped holds a special memory for me, June 5, 1944. Along in the afternoon we were called to assemble, and General Eisenhower, Ike, and Winston Churchill and a party of senior officers arrived at our staging area and they inspected the troops in our outfit, the paratroopers that were about to make the jump the next morning across the channel and into Normandy. And I just happened to be in one of the ranks. I'll never forget how, when Ike came down our rank, he paused in front of me for an instant and he winked, he winked at me and he said, «Good luck, soldier.»

Albert Hassenzahl, 101st Airborne Division
General Eisenhower was willing to visit the men about to land in Normandy one last time. The Supreme Commander of the Allied Expeditionary Force in Europe is dreading heavy losses: 50% killed or injured within the paratroopers and 70% within the infantry transported by gliders.

UTAH IN OPERATION
Overlord

In January 1943, while Nazi Germany occupies most of Europe, Roosevelt and Churchill meet in Casablanca and decide to organize a vast operation of landings in Europe. A few months later, the operation named Overlord is set to take place on May 1st, 1944 and is planned on three beaches of the bay of Seine. Indeed, Normandy coasts have the advantage of not being densely fortified, of being at the shelter of strong winds, and of offering long beaches of fine sand. The project takes shape and, at the beginning of 1944, Eisenhower and Montgomery decide to widen the Allied troops' sector of attack by adding two beaches: Sword in the East and Utah in the West.

General headquarter of the SHAEF (Supreme Headquarters Allied Expeditionary Force), February 1944. From left to right : General Bradley, Admiral Ramsay, Air Marshal Tedder, General Eisenhower, General Montgomery, Air Marshal Leigh-Mallory, General Bedell-Smith.

unequalled. At daybreak, once the bombardments were over, the attack on the beaches can start. According to the tide, it is on Utah, the most western beach, that the first wave of attack is launched.

Operation Neptune and Operation Overlord

Operation Neptune is the phase of attack of Operation Overlord. It brings together the operations of parachuting, of the landing of gliders and of the arrival by sea of heavy material intended for airborne divisions. Carried out during the night of June 5th to June 6th, at both ends of the landing sector, these first operations aim to protect the attack on the beaches and to cut off all lines of communication in order to prevent any German counter-offensive. The night before, the Allied

landing also experienced terrible air raids intended to destroy the artillery batteries of the Atlantic Wall. At dawn, the naval artillery takes over and, for 30 minutes, sets itself against the German defences still capable of firing. Despite the thousands of tons of released bombs, the effectiveness of these bombardments remains

Long beaches of fine sand favourable to landing are unfortunately often full of German defences (stakes, Czech hedgehogs, Belgian Gates…)

Emblems of the 101st and 82nd Airborne Divisions

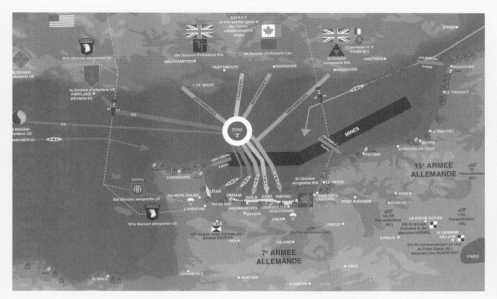

General Bradley and General Collins commanding the 7th Army Corps

Utah : a special operation !

Separated from the other beaches by the bay of Carentan, the landings on Utah make up a special operation. Located at the bottom of the Cotentin peninsula, this beach could have been a fallback position in case the landings on the other beaches would have failed. Eisenhower had planned to gather all the forces in a fit state to fight and to form a new bridgehead. Part of the troops would be charged to resist the Germans whereas another would advance toward Cherbourg, would seize the harbour and, after being joined by reinforcements, would allow a new offensive. However, the Allies did not need this safety plan, as each sector of landings fulfilled its mission.

YOUR MISSION WILL BE TO TAKE OVER AND GUARD BARQUETTE'S LOCK, AND BREVANDS' GANGWAYS FACING ISIGNY

General Collins' mission

Commanding the 7th American Army Corps, General Collins was commissioned to a very important mission: his men were to land on Utah beach, to link up with the bridgehead at Omaha, cut through the Cotentin peninsula by following a line from Carentan to Barneville and to seize Cherbourg's harbour. Having a deep water harbour will rapidly be essential for the supplies of the troops with material and fuel. At the head of two airborne divisions and of four infantry divisions, General Collins had a very well trained military strength and a good fighting quality.

General Maxwell Taylor commanding the 101st Airborne Division

American Troops
7th Army Corps (General Collins)
of the 1st US Army (General Bradley)
4th Infantry Division "Ivy Division" (General Barton)
9th Infantry Division "Old Reliable" (General Eddy)
90th Infantry Division "Tough Ombres" (General MacKelvie)
79th Infantry Division "Lorraine Cross" (General Wyche)

82nd Airborne Division "All American Division" (General Ridgway)
101st Airborne Division "Eagle Division" (General Taylor)

3

THE GERMAN OCCUPATION
in Normandy

In spring 1944, Normandy just like all of France is impatiently awaiting the Allied Landing. The German presence is increasingly unbearable. The civil population is suffering from shortages, restrictions and from an increasingly violent repression. Since the beginning of the occupation, D-Day has never been as much awaited; a waiting, full of hope and fear.

The Atlantic Wall Construction

As a strategic area, the coast of Normandy has been since 1942 a great building site reserved for the Todt organization in order to build the Atlantic Wall. The construction of these fortifications, normally able to stop a possible landing on the Western coasts of Europe, requires an abundant labour partly requisitioned within the population of Normandy. Artillery batteries, blockhaus, casemates, concrete dams, obstacles such as antitank mines, steel tetrahedrons, "Czech hedgehogs", kilometers of barbed wire, etc., hundreds of works strew the littoral. Marshall Erwin Rommel, at the head of group B armies in charge of the defence of the coasts of Europe, from the Loire to the Netherlands, carries out many visits of the Atlantic Wall and orders its reinforcement. He made people plant stakes in the fields behind the Wall to make the gilders crash and flooded thousands of hectars in which the Allied paratroopers would drown.

German soldiers stationed in a farm

HI MARCEL !

HI !

The weight of the occupation

The German presence had never been as strong in Normandy as it was in spring 1944. Between 150,000 and 200,000 German soldiers are positioned in the Channel and in Calvados. The 352nd and the 709th Infantry Divisions as well as the 6th Paratroop Regiment but also "voluntary" battalions from the East, Russians, Ukrainians, Cossacks and other Soviet populations who had rejoined the Wehrmacht can be found near the landing sector of Utah.

German requisitions

The rise of tensions can be explained by the requisitioning in the countryside for the soldiery, food shortage linked to the monopolization of resources by the occupant, forced labour for the troops, hunting for STO* resistants, summary arrests as well as the repression which beats down more and more violently against the resistance. The Normans are impatiently waiting for the Allied landing and the Liberation even if they fear its consequences and the potential sacrifices they will have to put up with.

*forced labour instituted in France by the Nazis during World War II (in Robert & Collins Senior, 2002)

Life during occupation

I do not know if one can talk about unconsciousness, but nobody was afraid in Condé-sur-Noireau. Life wasn't too bad. Everybody had relatives living in farms and there weren't any food shortages. We regularly sent supplies to our Parisian correspondents. The Germans weren't violent. Like all the young people of Condé, I was required to plant Rommel's asparaguses, 4 km out of town. It was good when we planted one a day. The German sentries didn't say anything; they would rather take the pickaxe. The Kommandantur only got angry once. They made us work on Whit Sunday, on 4th June 1944, even if there were communions.

Maurice Piard, 18 years old in June 1944, in 1944 l'été de la liberté, Ouest France, 1994.

German troops at Mont-Saint-Michel

They arrived in Caen and they marched downtown, in ranks of five. Big guys, tanned, who were singing with several voices, to perfection. They were expressing friendship, discipline, power. All the contrary to our soldiers that we had seen just before, in a panic, badly shod, badly shaven, feverish, badly dressed, sometimes without weapons. The first act of resistance was to refuse to be seduced, to be eaten, to say yes, these are the people we need, as I heard from the mouths of some friends [...] Resistance didn't come from shame for us, but from a sorrow. We started by looking for abandoned weapons given up during retreatment, by sticking abusive propaganda brochures for the Germans, then we handed out a newspaper, pictures of De Gaulle, whom we didn't know, but whose voice, engaging and clear, summed up all our feelings.

Jacques Vico, Resistance fighter, in L'Ouest en guerre, Ouest France, 1994.

PARATROOPERS DURING THE NIGHT
from June 5ᵗʰ to June 6ᵗʰ

During the night from June 5ᵗʰ to June 6ᵗʰ 1944, the 82ⁿᵈ and 101ˢᵗ American Airborne divisions, in the West, as well as the 6th British Paratrooper division, in the East, are released, behind the beaches, at both ends of the landing sector. Their mission? Seize the bridges, the roads and crossroads in order to allow the troops arriving from the sea to come inland.

Paratroopers of the 82ⁿᵈ Airborne division on board of a C-47

The decisive role of the scouts

In charge of marking out the parachuting areas in Normandy, the 360 scouts or pathfinders are quickly confronted with a very difficult situation. The fog and the clouds disrupt the pilots and the firings of the FLAK* force them to carry out droppings both at altitudes too high or too low and at too high speeds. As a result, the paratroopers are scattered on the sector and there is a heavy loss of material. On the ground, the floods in the marshes and the presence of "Rommel's asparaguses", wooden stakes topped by mines or linked together with cables, finishes off the disorganization of the landing of the men. Scattered all over the sector, the pathfinders struggle over their mission to mark out the sector. However, this mission is essential to help out the arrival of the paratroopers.

Paratroopers jump on Sainte-Mère-Eglise

Close behind the pathfinders, the 82ⁿᵈ and 101ˢᵗ Airborne divisions commanded by General Ridgway and General Taylor, i.e. about 13,000 men, fly over Normandy. The men of the 82ⁿᵈ division are released around Sainte-Mère-Eglise and their mission is to take over the small town as well as the bridges spanning Merderet. As for the 101ˢᵗ division, it is released not far from Sainte-Marie-du-Mont. Their goal is to neutralize an artillery batterie, to

Concentrated on their mission, the paratroopers are ready for the jump

*FLAK : abbreviation of FLiegerAbwehrKanone meaning anti-aircraft cannon

conquer the ground to the coast in order to facilitate the advancing of the troops landing on Utah beach. Unfortunately, a greatest confusion prevails on the ground. The Americans find it impossible to gather all their men, and the Germans are so confused that the counter-offensive cannot be held. The occupying troops give up the defence of the coast for a few hours in order to go after the paratroopers.

We were very close to disaster!

The droppings were hastened and vague and therefore the paratroopers were scattered over 20 km, putting a large number of men out of the action. Killed by the enemy before even touching the ground, drowned in the flooded

marshes or captured after being betrayed by the clickety clack of the "grasshoppers" when they were trying to assemble, very few paratroopers end up joining the rallying

points. In the morning of June 6th, 1,000 of the 6,000 men of the 101st division had reached one of the points. For those who are too far away, they improvise and sometimes wander several days through fields, looking for their unit, while trying to avoid the German patrols. During the first hours of the landings, the situation of the Allied troops seems very close to disaster, but this dispersion, which spreads disorder in the German defence, rapidly becomes a real advantage.

Lined up behind each other, the gliders are loaded with men and material

This Waco glider carrying infantrymen crashed near Hiesville. General Pratt, Assistant Commander of the 101st Airborne division, is also killed in the crash of his glider on June 6th 1944

Waco gliders

Airborne divisions receive the support of a new weapon, the glider, whose astonishing history starts in 1941. Composed of a metal frame, of pieces of wood and tight fabric, the glider is a real technical achievement. Tractor-drawn by a plane and released around ten miles from its goal, it flies without noise and can carry a loading heavier than its weight. Bearing the name of the company which built them, the Waco gliders can shelter 15 infantrymen or a jeep and its crew. Two infantry regiments as well as material will be brought in as reinforcements by gliders.

Grasshopper : small metal object that the paratroopers were equipped with and that emitted a "clickety clack" which was easily identifiable, allowing them to recognize each other.

UTAH BEACH, *0630 hours*

In the final hours of the night, a last bombardment on Normandy's coast was carried out by almost 300 marauders of the 9th Air Force who unloaded 4,500 tons of bombs on the artillery batteries of the Atlantic Wall. At daybreak, the naval artillery took over and the warships pounded the German defences that were still in a position to fire.

Utah Beach, 0630 hours. The landing sector seems so quiet that the GIs of the 8th Regiment of the 4th Division come out of the water, gun on their shoulder.

Contrary to what occurs at the same time at Omaha Beach, the American units landed on Utah count weak losses.

A landing fleet adrift!

Set for 0630 hours, an hour after the beginning of the rising tide, the attack of the Allied troops on Utah could start. Unfortunately, a strong lateral current lead the small flat-bottomed boats away from the landing sector. Tossed by the waves and obstructed by the TLC'*s manoeuvres which were trying to bring the amphibious tanks as close as possible to the shore, the boats drifted almost two kilometers south. Beached at Madeleine and not at the dunes of Varraville, the first detachments of the 4th American Infantry Division dismount on the beach at the expected time. This hitch finally appears to be favourable to the GIs who land on a coast which is less fortified and less exposed to the batteries of Azeville and Saint-Marcouf. The first wave composed of 4 Infantry companies, supported by 2 DD Tank** companies is followed by, five mi-nutes later, the second wave, then the third and the fourth.

A successful landing

At 0630 hours, in the wake of the landing of the 1st battalion of the 8th Infantry Regiment, on the right, on Green Beach, and of the 2nd battalion which dismounts on the left, on Read Beach, about thirty amphibious tanks arrived, launched three kilometers offshore. The weak German resistance enables them to quickly control the ground, to clear away the obstacles on the beach and to facilitate the access inside the country by arranging exits from the beach. The demolition teams equipped with bulldozers open breaches in the anti-tank concrete wall and arrange parking areas for the vehicles. Wooden slopes, stakes and tetrahedrons made out of concrete are realized; paths cleared of mines are materialized. Despite the sporadic firing from

the coastal defences, the landing went as expected. Everything seemed so calm that the GIs of the 8th Regiment of the 4th Infantry Division came out of the water, a gun on the shoulder or slung across the shoulder. At 0800 hours, over

In the morning, while some men take a little rest, others cross the anti-tank wall that closes the beach to go into the dunes.

600 meters of beach were free and around 0930 hours, the beach was completely clear.

The link-up with the paratroopers

Whereas the first troops progress toward the beach exits, the landing of the men and equipment continued. The shooting from the German batteries of Azeville and Saint-Marcouf, although with little provisions, still obstructed the American troops from dismounting on the beach. The link-up with the paratroopers occured during the day, for instance the contact in Sainte-Marie-du-Mont occured in the middle of the day.

A paratrooper of the 101st American Airborne Division holds in respect a German combatant.

A fulfilled mission

The landing on Utah is a success. The losses are not as bad as the ones at Omaha. As the air raids and naval bombardments disorganized the German defence, the reaction of the coastal batteries of the Atlantic Wall is

weak. The batteries of Azeville and Saint-Marcouf remained the most dangerous but they ceased fire around June 8th. Turned into German retrenched camps, they showed a fierce resistance which delayed the advance of

A paratrooper is running toward the porch of the church in Sainte-Mère-Eglise, could an isolated German sniper still be taking refuge in the church tower?

the 4th Infantry Division toward Cherbourg. Despite a few hitches, the initially planned mission was fulfilled: the link-up with the paratroopers was achieved, road RN13 was reached and the ascent toward Cherbourg could start.

*TLC: Tank Landing Craft
**DD Tank: Duplex Drive amphibious tank

General Theodore Roosevelt

General Roosevelt, eldest son of the president of the United States Th. Roosevelt (1858-1919), is the only officer of this rank to land with the first wave of attack. Second commander of the 4th Infantry Division, he insists upon his superiors to be with his men and declares "It will reassure the kids to know I am near them". Showing coolness and initiative when the troops are sent down south, Roosevelt, after having looked into the situation, declares with satisfaction "The war will start here!". General Roosevelt, who died of a heart attack in July 1944, is buried in the American cemetery of Colleville-sur-mer.

FIRST LIBERATIONS
and meetings with the Normans

The day after D-Day, the Allies have to consolidate their position, to complete the link-up of the different landing areas and to widen bridge heads. Despite the worries of the Allied staff on how the civilians were going to react after the terrible bombardments, the people from Normandy delivered a warm welcome to their liberators.

YES, BUT WE HAVE BEEN WARNED TO KEEP OUR EYES OPEN ON THE CIVILIANS OF THE COASTAL AREAS WHO STAYED PUT... THEY MIGHT BE COLLABORATORS...

Consolidate one's position

The landing of the 4th Infantry Division at Utah is a success. The infantrymen complete the link-up with the Airborne troops of the 101st in Poupeville at midday of the 6th of June. Scattered and isolated in the middle of the swamps of Merderet, starting to lack munitions, the paratroopers of the 82nd complete the link-up with more difficulty. Despite pockets of German resistance, like in the sector of Turqueville, Carquebut or Saint-Côme-du-Mont, and despite a counter-attack to try to take back Sainte-Mère-Eglise from the Americans since the middle of the night, a bridgehead is established. But it has to be consolidated and Carentan, still in the hands of the

Germans, can be defined as an "area" between Utah and Omaha that has to be taken.

Scene of happiness of the freedom

"Now, take Carentan!"

When General Taylor informs General Collins that Saint-Côme-du-Mont is finally under control, the latter orders "Very good, now, take Carentan". The mission is confided to the men of 101st Airborne Division. To do so, the hardened paratroopers of Colonel von der Heydte engage fierce battles, including the use of knives, hidden in farms or behind hedges. During the morning of 12th June, the first paratroopers enter Carentan, town

Freedom of Carentan

strongly victim of bombardments. A last counter-attack, launched by the grenadiers of the 17th SS Division, fails the next day thanks to the intervention of armoured vehicles coming from Omaha.

The situation 6 days after

On 12th June, with a real bridgehead from west to east of 100 kilometers long and from 10 to 30 kilometers large as well as a total control of the air, the Allied troops have a significant strategic advantage. Rommel, who is addressing the German higher command that day, summarizes the situation by writing: "Our air force and our navy are unable to carry out a valid opposition. The enemy is much more quickly rein-

rated villages. Children experience the joy of chewing gum or tasting chocolate and coca-cola. Adults smoke American cigarettes. In the towns not too ravaged by the liberating battles, the local jubilation is shown in improvised dances. An eternal gratefulness appears enthusiastically toward the young American soldiers ready to give up their lives for freedom.

forced compared to the arrival of our reserves… Our position is extremely difficult to hold".

The Normans and their liberators

The first meetings with the Americans and the people from Normandy who have finally been released are full of reserve on either side. After several years of occupation, of Vichy regime and of German propaganda, are the French really friends? The GI's were told to beware of the civilians. Soldier Lloyd D. Lane writes: "We don't dare trust anybody". The initial battles and bombardments destroyed so many towns and thousands of locals are already dead because of the bombs. How can

you then fully express the joy of being free?
But quickly, glasses of cider and

The soldiers taste with pleasure Calvados and Cider

bottles of Calvados are appreciated by the American soldiers. Hastily made, Star-Spangled Banners decorate the windows of the libe-

Normandy children dressed in the colours of the American flag taste sweets given by a GI

We sympathize rather easily with the children and sometimes we even meet French people and even schoolboys speaking English [...] Children get it very quickly, they started asking for sweets [...] Some of them have learned English in school. We have of course learned a few French words, but we especially communicate with gestures.

Excerpt from a letter from Lloyd D. Lane

FROM PEN *to Gun*

Every soldier writes to his relatives, sometimes several times a day. These letters are emotionally essential to "survive". In their letters, the soldiers describe what they see and what they go through. Mail connects them to the past, to normal life, the one they lived before and that they hope to find after the war. Soldiers' letters are a striking and concrete testimony of everyday life. They make the private life of the soldiers easier to understand. Thanks to them, seldom asked questions easily find personal answers: what does one think of at first when one kills a man? How does one go through a day knowing it could be the last?

Mail of victory

In order to allow the American soldiers to communicate with their families as fast as possible, the clever system of V mail (mail of victory) is developed and takes effect as from June 1942. The postal bags that used to carry normal letters were too voluminous in the ships' holds, at the expense of the troops' supplies. The postal service of the American army drew its inspiration from the sort of mail (Airgraph) used by the British forces since 1940. The soldiers write their letters on a specific form which is then microfilmed.

V mail enables the reduction of the mail volume to transport. One bag replaces the 37 postal bags that were needed to send 150,000 one page letters. This system also works from the United States to Europe and ensures a quick mail service. Between June, 15th 1942 and April, 1st 1945, more than 510 million V mails were sent by soldiers to their families in the United States and more than 556 million were sent from the United States to military posts abroad. Every American soldier received an average of 40 letters a month.

Mail censure

Censure of mail is applied in every single army at war. Indeed, information such as material data, names of places, battle dates, etc.

must not be revealed in letters. This information could badly influence the morale of those receiving it or be a source of information if ever it got into the enemy's hands, and is therefore removed by the service in charge of the censure.

Read and write to stay alive

Writing to prevent from dying

However, some information is not censured. Thus, through letters, the war can be lived indirectly. Writing for the soldier, and whatever the subject is, is a form of freedom, relief, therapy. Writing one's name on the walls of a camp, having a tattoo of the name of one's relatives are examples of traces or signs left by the soldiers to ward off death. He often doesn't mention massacres, sufferings and fear in his letters in order to prevent his relatives from worrying. But letters can also clearly broach the premonition of disappearance and death.

The three dots and a dash represent the "V" of Victory in the Morse code

German soldiers resting in a bunker

Dear Parents, Dear Brothers and Sister,

Your son, your brother expresses all his affection to you! I greet you. Apart from my wound, I am feeling well again. I hope you are also well. On Tuesday, June 6th, there was an unprecedented attack, an attack one cannot imagine, one that had never been seen before, even in Russia [...] Each one of us did everything he could to counter the American superiority. I must have shot in bursts more than four hundred times, three hundred of which were tracer bullets. The 100 to 250 meters which separated us from the attackers were favourable to us. That's all for today! Lots of love! Your loving son and brother.

Franz Gockel is 18 at the time of the landing. After 6 hours of fierce combat, his hand is pierced by an American bullet. Evacuated, he is sent back to the front in Alsace and finishes the war captured by the American in November 1944.

Dear Mom, Pop and family,

Now that I am actually here I see that the chances of my returning to all of you are quite slim, therefore I want to write this letter now while I am yet able. I want you to know how much I love each of you. You mean everything to me and it is the realization of your love that gives me the courage to continue. [...] Remember always that I love you each most fervently and I am proud of you. Consider, Mary, my wife, as having taken my place in the family circle and watch over each other. Love to my family

Letter from Jack Lundberg to his family, 19th May 1944. Head observer on a B17, Jack Lundberg disappears during a mission in July 1944. His body is found only 9 months after his death. He is buried in the cemetery of Saint-Laurent. Letters from D-Day, The Guardian, Friday 28 May 2004.

THE RESISTANCE
in action booklet

In 1944, the French Resistance was finalizing its organization. Early February, the different underground forces united and formed the French Forces of The Interior (FFI) under the command of General Koenig and under the authority of General De Gaulle.

Post D-Day poster paying tribute to the FFI (French Forces of the Interior).

The "Brutus network"

This important resistance network was created in Marseille in 1941. It then spread to the entire French territory and became, from 1943, a national network. With the strength of over 1,000 agents, it carried out a great variety of missions including intelligence, organization of escape lines and military action.

in Normandy? Did new divisions arrive? What effect had the aerial bombardments on the morale of the enemy? The resisters who rubbed shoulders with the Germans on a daily basis were the only ones able to supply London with that precious information.

Informing the Allies

To prepare the assault in Normandy, the Allies needed precise intelligence on the road network, bridges, railway lines, the Atlantic Wall's defenses, which would increase day by day, and on the military power of the German army. Numerous reconnaissance missions were organized and millions of aerial photographs were sent to England. It was all there, or at least almost…as some information was still missing. What was the strength of the German units

The big day!

Every night, the resisters would listen to the BBC, hoping to hear messages announcing the landing. In early June, there was no doubt: the English radio broadcasted several coded messages signaling to them that the assault in Normandy was imminent. For the

Derailment of a train.

Resistance, the time had come to act. "The Dice are on the carpet", launched Plan Green, which was to sabotage the rails; then "it's hot in Suez", launched Plan Tortoise, which was to block the roads; as for Plan Purple, cut off telephone lines. Everywhere small groups of FFI resisters took action: rails were unbolted, warning signs were reversed, trees were felled across the roads…On the night of the 5th, we counted close to a thousand sabotage actions all over France. It is assumed today, that the sabotage of the rails and communications

Crystal receiver set, hidden in a can.

made the Germans lose precious time and delayed the arrival of reinforcements in Normandy by 48 hours.

Mere civilians and resisters

During the Battle of Normandy, the resisters continued their actions. They guided stray soldiers, supplied information about the German positions or rescued pilots shot down by the FLAK, civilians also became actors of the resistance. The German occupier, who understood what role the local population could play, arrested numerous suspects. Most of them were quickly released after having been interrogated, however, one third received a heavy sentence.

Between June and August 1944, while the battle was raging, the German repression against civilians became more severe and summary executions multiplied, making a total of 1,600 victims.

"The long sobs of autumn's violins…"

Contrary to popular belief, the coded message starting with these Verlaine verses did not announce the landing to all the resisters in France, but only to a group based in Northern France. The German 15th German Army had deciphered the message and knew that the assault was imminent.

Young resistance fighters learning how to use a weapon.

A resistance fighter preparing the sabotage of the rails.

MEMORY OF THE LANDING

Thanks to steles, plaques, cemeteries and memorials, the memory of those who had landed and fought in Normandy and who had sometimes lost their lives to bring freedom, was marked right after the Liberation. Thus, hundreds of thousands of people come every year to the landing areas to honour the memory of the soldiers and to try to understand this exceptional worldwide event. Other ways are movies, American television series or video games that also constitute a form of knowledge and of appropriation of this history.

Monument in the shape of a star with five branches, the Mardasson is erected in Bastogne, Belgium, near the last stone marker of Liberty Road

Emblematic museums

Museums relate the actions of the 82nd and the 101st Airborne Divisions as well as the landing operation of the American troops on Utah Beach. Thus, with its two architecture-emblematic buildings, one in the shape of a parachute sheltering a Waco glider, the other in the shape of a delta wing sheltering a Douglas C47 Argonia plane, the Airborne Troops museum of Sainte-Mère-Eglise is an anthem to the courage of the American paratroopers. On Madeleine beach in Sainte-Marie-du-Mont, the museum of Utah Beach, established on the landing sector of the American Navy, surrounded by American

Museum of the Airborne troops in Sainte-Mère-Eglise

war monuments is a starting point toward the path to freedom.

Museum of Utah Beach

The path to freedom

The Liberty stone markers mark out, from Sainte-Mère-Eglise (stone marker "0") and Utah Beach (stone marker "00") to Bastogne, Belgium, the route of the 3rd American army commanded by General Patton. This road is materialized by a series of milestones, made out of concrete

Liberty stone markers - Stone marker "00" at Utah Beach and stone marker 1145 in Bastogne, Belgium

and symbolizing the Liberty flame which is coming out of the water just like the American youth landed on Normandy beaches in 1944.

The Church of Sainte-Mère-Eglise

Thanks to its two stained glass windows commemorating the liberation of the soldiers of the 82nd Airborne Division and its model hanging from the tower, pointing out the story of the parachutist John Steele, the church of Sainte-Mère-Eglise is a religious monument fully participating in the memory works.

The church of Sainte-Mère-Eglise with the model of the paratrooper John Steele

We would like to thank Rémy Desquesnes, historian and Marie-Claude Berthelot for their proof-reading and iconographic research. We also thank the Mémorial de Caen for their scientific and pedagogic expertise.

Credits Photographs :
I. Bournier : 14
Bundesarchiv Koblenz : 4, 5, 13
NARA : 1, 2, 3, 6, 7, 8, 9, 10, 11, 12
Mémorial de Caen : 2, 3, 5, 13
© Musée Utah Beach : 16
© P.Y. Le Meur/Airborne Museum : 16